Kenny Kangaroo

Dave and Pat Sargent are longtime residents of Prairie Grove, Arkansas. Dave, a fourth-generation dairy farmer, began writing in early December 1990, and Pat, a former teacher, began writing shortly after. They enjoy the outdoors and have a real love for animals.

Kenny Kangaroo

By

Dave and Pat Sargent

Illustrated by
Jane Lenoir

Ozark Publishing, Inc.
P.O. Box 228
Prairie Grove, AR 72753

Library of Congress Cataloging-in-Publication Data

Sargent, Dave, 1941-
  Kenny Kangaroo / by Dave and Pat Sargent ; illustrated
by Jane Lenoir.
       p. cm.—(Animal pride series)
Summary: After his circus train derails and releases
him into the Arkansas countryside, Kenny Kangaroo
discovers that not all animals like to be punched in the
nose. Includes factual information about kangaroos.
  ISBN 1-56763-539-3 (hardcover)—ISBN 1-56763-
540-7 (pbk.)
  [1. Kangaroos—Fiction. 2. Animals—Fiction. 3.
Arkansas--Fiction.] I.
Sargent, Pat, 1936—II. Lenoir, Jane, 1946— ill. III.
Title.
  PZ7.S2465 Ke 2000
  [Fic]—dc21
                                    00-011483

Printed in the United States of America

Inspired by

watching kangaroos hop around in zoos and punch each other, for fun. They are very entertaining to watch but we wouldn't want one mad at us, would we?

Dedicated to

all students who have ever had a fight with a good friend or maybe someone who is not a good friend. Hold your punches. Think about it. As you read this book, maybe you'll learn something from this kangaroo!

Foreword

After the circus train derails, Kenny Kangaroo can't find his friends. But he's having so much fun going around punching everyone that he doesn't really mind being separated from them.

A kangaroo might punch a man or a little beaver, but when he starts boxing a wild mustang and a mean Jersey bull in the nose, things start popping!

Contents

Kenny Kangaroo

If you would like to have the authors of the Animal Pride Series visit your school, free of charge, call 1-800-321-5671 or 1-800-960-3876.

One

The Boxing Kangaroo!

Kenny Kangaroo looked right and left before hopping across the road. His alert eyes sparkled with excitement, and his nose sniffed the clean country air. His ears twitched back and forth as he listened for strange and dangerous sounds. He held his small forearms against his chest as his large and powerful back legs sprang his buff-colored body forward.

He hopped over a fence and leaned over to have a bite of lush green grass. He was so busy that he

1

failed to notice a beautiful white horse who was grazing nearby.

"Hello, stranger," a friendly voice called. "Welcome to Arkansas country!"

Kenny Kangaroo jerked his head up. His eyes were glazed with immediate anger as he looked around for the critter.

"You must be new to these parts. My name is White Thunder, Pal. I'm a wild mustang," the horse said as he walked toward Kenny. "What's your name? Or better yet, what are you? I saw you jump that fence. I can do that, but I don't!"

The kangaroo did not respond. He waited until the big white horse stopped in front of him, and then he leaned back on his strong, thick tail. And a second later, his left paw shot out and hit White Thunder smack in the nose.

"Hey!" the mustang yelled. "Why did you do that? I was trying to be friendly."

"Humph," the boxing kangaroo scoffed. "Friendly is no fun." Then, he suddenly smiled before adding, "But fighting is! I love to fight!"

White Thunder rubbed his sore nose on his front leg before looking at Kenny.

"It's kind of hard to fight when I don't have a reason," he mumbled. "At least tell me who you are."

"Sure," the kangaroo agreed. "I'm Kenny. Kenny Kangaroo. And," he added sternly, "I don't need a reason to fight. It is just what I do best."

"But why?" the white horse asked. "Why do you like to fight? Do you actually enjoy fighting?"

"Because it's so much fun!" Kenny squealed and again slugged White Thunder on his nose.

"Ouch!" the horse bellowed. "Let me explain something to you. If you act terrible, others will not like you. Where are you from? Why are you so ornery?"

"Well," Kenny said, "I was born a long way from here in a place called Australia. But now, I live in this country; this place called the U.S.A. I'm a member of the circus but our train had a wreck. I'm lost," he said with a grin, "but I'm not really too worried." He waved his short arm toward a distant meadow. "Looks like there's plenty of food around here."

"That's true," the white horse agreed and nodded his head.

"But animals around here do not live on food alone. We all need friends," White Thunder said. Then

6

he glared at Kenny Kangaroo before adding, "And I don't mean strangers who go around punching someone in the nose for no reason."

"Okay. I'll not punch you in the nose anymore," Kenny promised. "Now will you be my friend?"

"That's better," the white horse muttered. "Yes, I'll be your friend." He paused before adding in a gruff voice, "As long as you understand that you must not fight."

Kenny looked at the ground and shuffled a huge hind foot in the dirt.

"I will not fight you," he said. "So, will you help me find my circus train?"

White Thunder neighed and pawed the earth. "I can take you to someone who will. Farmer John and Molly are good folks, and they will help you. They live nearby."

"Great!" the kangaroo squealed. "Let's go!"

Two

Billy Gets Punched!

An hour later, the buff-colored kangaroo and the big white horse stopped beside a stream for a drink. A beaver was chomping on the trunk of a tree.

"Hello, friends," the beaver called. "How are you today?"

Before White Thunder even had a chance to reply, Kenny Kangaroo leapt in front of the beaver. His right paw punched the beaver in the nose. As the little fellow rolled backward, White Thunder's teeth sank into the kangaroo's posterior.

"Ouch!" Kenny squawked, sort of like a chicken. "That hurt!"

"Good!" was White Thunder's reply. "Now you know how that poor little beaver feels. You must stop punching everybody!"

The kangaroo again looked at the ground and shuffled his huge back foot in the dirt.

"Shame on you, Kenny," the horse scolded as he walked over to the bewildered little beaver.

"I think Kenny is sorry that he punched you, Billy. Are you okay?"

The beaver rubbed his nose with one paw and nodded his head.

"Just get that big bully away from my pond, White Thunder," the furry little critter muttered. "I don't want him anywhere near my lodge. I don't like him!"

Kenny Kangaroo gulped as White Thunder glared at him and motioned for him to follow.

"I'm real sorry," Kenny whined as he hopped into step behind the horse.

"Don't be sorry!" the mustang bellowed. "Just be nice!"

Later the traveling twosome started up the lane to Farmer John's house. Suddenly Kenny Kangaroo saw a strange critter in the pasture. He leaped the fence and hopped straight toward a cow who was calmly grazing. Without warning, the kangaroo slugged the cow in the nose. Before she knew what had hit her, he was hopping toward a large bull standing nearby. Satan the Bull shook his head at Kenny, but the determined kangaroo stopped in front of Satan and leaned back on his powerful tail. He giggled as he punched the bull on the nose.

When Kenny saw the bull begin pawing the ground, he laughed and hopped back over the fence.

The kangaroo's feet had just hit the ground when ole Satan charged. His horns crashed into the fence right where Kenny had been!

"You were lucky that time, Kenny," the mustang said gruffly. "Satan the Bull might have gored you. He could have killed you! What's wrong with you, anyhow? You promised that you would not punch anyone anymore."

"I meant that I would not punch you anymore," the kangaroo said as he laughed. "I haven't had this much fun for a long time."

"If you don't stop fighting, Kenny," White Thunder warned, "you're going to get in **bad** trouble!"

Minutes later, they stopped beside the barn door.

"You wait here," the mustang ordered. "I'll go find Farmer John."

"Okay," the kangaroo agreed. "I won't move from this spot."

As the horse walked around the side of the barn and disappeared from view, Kenny looked at the neat buildings. He listened to a songbird who was perched in a tall tree near the chicken house. He admired the brightly colored rooster and enjoyed the soft, happy clucking of the hens.

A sudden loud noise from inside the big hay barn startled him. He leaned back on his powerful tail. He shut his eyes real tight. His paw clenched into a tight fist.

"No, Kenny!" White Thunder screamed. "That's Farmer John!"

But the warning came too late. The kangaroo's fist slammed into the midsection of the startled man.

When Kenny opened his eyes, he gulped. The fellow was slumped over, holding his sore stomach and gasping for breath.

The kangaroo suddenly realized what he had done. He felt sorrow. Kenny groaned and quickly hopped away from the gasping Farmer John. He turned and silently stared at the man who could have helped him.

"Oh mercy me," he whispered. "I should not have done that. I hope he'll be okay."

A woman's sudden scream pierced the stillness.

"John!" Molly yelled. "What in the world happened? Are you all right?"

The man was unable to answer as he fought to fill his lungs with air.

Molly ran to Farmer John's side

and knelt down. His face was white, and his breath was returning in short gasps.

"I don't know what hit me," Farmer John finally sputtered, "but I'm declaring war against it."

Kenny gulped and then hopped around the side of the barn. Seconds later, he cautiously peeked to see what was happening. The horse motioned for him to hide.

Kenny gulped and nodded before hopping toward the back of the barn. He found a small opening between two haystacks and crawled inside. His shoulders shook and his teeth chattered as he waited for White Thunder. Tears began rolling down his cheeks as he recalled the hard punch he had delivered to Farmer John's stomach.

The sun was setting on the western horizon when he finally heard the familiar whinny of the horse.

"Kenny, come out from your hiding place. I need to talk to you."

Minutes later, the kangaroo and the horse were standing nose to nose.

"You do know," White Thunder said, "that you are in big trouble with Farmer John?"

"Y - yes," Kenny sniffled.

"Have you learned anything, Kenny?" White Thunder asked in a gruff voice.

"Y - yes," Kenny Kangaroo stuttered. "I don't want to fight anymore."

"Good," the horse murmured. "Now listen closely. I have a plan that may get you out of this mess."

Three

Kenny's Sore Paws

Thirty minutes later, the horse led the humble kangaroo through the barnyard and into the walnut grove.

"It's harvest time for farmers," White Thunder explained. "Now, Farmer John was trying to find help with the walnut harvest, and I feel that you owe him a big favor."

"Yes," Kenny agreed. "I do. But what can I do about his walnut harvest?"

Kenny saw a smile on his friend's face for the first time in many hours.

"Well, since you are so good at punching and hitting, you can put your talent to use," the mustang said. "How about knocking those walnuts down from the tree limbs in this orchard?"

The repentant kangaroo did not hesitate. He immediately went to work on the walnut trees. He smiled as the nuts clattered to the ground because he knew that Farmer John would be surprised when he realized that the nuts had been harvested.

The sun was peeking over the eastern horizon, casting lavender, gold, and pink hues across the sky when Kenny punched and hit the last nut tree in the orchard. He hurriedly gathered the walnuts into a burlap sack and set it beside the low row of harvested nuts.

"Whew!" Kenny muttered as he gazed at his night's work. "I'm tired and my paws are sore."

Kenny heard a chuckle echo through the silence of early morning.

"You did a fine job, Kenny," White Thunder said. "I'm proud of you, my friend."

Kenny gulped and hopped over to the mustang. "Is Farmer John going to be okay?" he asked.

"He's fine," White Thunder replied. "He'll be even better when he sees your harvesting job."

A deep voice interrupted their conversation. "Look! The walnuts are harvested! They are off the trees and packed in burlap sacks!"

Kenny started to run and hide, but White Thunder shook his head.

"You'll be okay, Kenny," he muttered. "Just stay where you are."

Molly was running fast when she suddenly noticed the kangaroo. She screeched to a halt and pointed.

"Where did he come from? We better call the zoo to come get him."

Farmer John put his arm over her shoulder and stared at Kenny.

"Hmmm," he said. "This may explain who punched me yesterday. And, it may also explain how the walnuts were harvested." He patted Kenny on the head. "Yep, I think this fellow punched me, but I also believe he punched the walnut trees. Thank you, big fellow."

Farmer John chuckled. "The newspaper told that a kangaroo is still missing from the train wreck. I'll take him to his circus friends."

As Kenny and White Thunder followed the couple back toward the house, the horse asked, "Isn't it fun to be nice, Kenny?"

"Yes," Kenny said with a grin. "You know, I truly enjoy being nice. It's even more fun than fighting!"

Kenny rubbed his sore paws and grinned. And, he thought, it's not painful. It hurts my paws when I punch someone, so I'm going to be a nice kangaroo and stop fighting. Life is good!

Four

Kangaroo Facts

Kangaroo is a common name for certain marsupial animals found in Australia and neighboring islands. Typical large kangaroos have sheep-like heads; large, movable ears; very slender chests; and heavy hind parts. They have short front legs with five unequal digits, and long, powerful hind legs with tendons that act like springs for energy-efficient hopping. A big kangaroo can cover a distance of 30 feet in a single leap. The hind feet typically have four toes; one digit bears a long, sharp claw used in defense. A large kangaroo, usually timid, is dangerous when at bay, hitting its attacker with its forepaws and slashing out with its strong hind legs. Its long, muscular tail is used for balance when it leaps and for support when it sits or walks. The tough hide is covered with soft fur.

Females have special pouches. A newborn, called a joey, finds its way into its mother's pouch, where it stays until it is five to nine months old. The pouch has four mammary glands. Two at a time are functional. The joey emerges at from six to ten months old, but will stay with mama, continuing to suckle by placing its head in her pouch, until it is twelve to eighteen months old.

The best-known and largest species are the giant, or great gray, and the red, or woolly, kangaroo. Both species reach a length of about five feet, not counting the tail, which may be up to four feet long in the giant kangaroo.

Another large species, called the wallaroo, is somewhat stouter. Large kangaroos are terrestrial grazing animals that subsist chiefly on vegetation. Sheep ranchers have claimed that they damage grazing lands, but this could be contributed to the sheep.

Kangaroos of smaller size, called wallabies, are usually brighter in color than the large species. Many of these are about the size of a rabbit; some so resemble rabbits that they are called hare wallabies.

ROCK WALLABY

The nail-tailed wallabies, so called because their tails are tipped with a horny nail, and the relatively short-tailed pademelons are two other types of wallabies. The red-necked wallaby inhabits thickets, whereas the rock wallabies live in crevices in rocks. The rock wallabies are chiefly nocturnal. The only arboreal kangaroos are the small tree kangaroos, whose front legs are almost as long as their hind legs.

These marsupials seem awkward in making their way either on the ground or in trees, but they prefer an arboreal habitat.

TREE KANGAROO

The potoroos, or rat kangaroos, are small animals that resemble jumping rats. Many of the species, although terrestrial, have a prehensile tail. Two examples are the long-nosed potoroo and the short-nosed rat kangaroo, also known as boodie or burrowing bettong.

BURROWING BETTONG

The musk kangaroo is a rat-like wallaby living in the rain forest of northern coastal Queensland. It has five toes on each hind foot and a mostly naked and scaly tail. This animal may be a link between the kangaroo and the related phalanger.

MUSK KANGAROO

Amazing Athletes ✧ Atletas increíbles

David Ortiz

Baseball Star ✧ Estrella del béisbol

Mary Ann Hoffman

Traducción al español: Eduardo Alamán

PowerKiDS press™ & **Editorial Buenas Letras**™
New York

Published in 2007 by The Rosen Publishing Group, Inc.
29 East 21st Street, New York, NY 10010

Book Design: Daniel Hosek
Layout Design: Lissette González

Photo Credits: Cover, p. 11 © Otto Greule Jr./Getty Images; p. 5 © Al Bello/Getty Images; p. 7 © Jamie Squire/Getty Images; p. 9 © Craig Melvin/Allsport; p. 13 © Donald Miralle/ Getty Images; pp. 15, 17 © Jed Jacobsohn/Getty Images; p. 19 © Jonathan Daniel/ Getty Images; p. 21 © Doug Pensinger/Getty Images.

Library of Congress Cataloging-in-Publication Data

Hoffman, Mary Ann, 1947-
  David Ortiz : baseball star / Mary Ann Hoffman.; traducción al español: Eduardo Alamán — 1st ed.
    p. cm. - (Amazing Athletes / Atletas increíbles)
  Includes index.
  ISBN-13: 978-1-4042-7599-7
  ISBN-10: 1-4042-7599-1
  1. Ortiz, David, 1975-—Juvenile literature. 2. Baseball players—Dominican Republic—Biography— Juvenile literature. 3. Spanish-language materials I. Title. II. Series.

Manufactured in the United States of America

Contents

Contenido

David Ortiz is a big man and a powerful hitter. He is called Big Papi.

David Ortiz es un hombre muy robusto y un bateador muy poderoso. Por eso le llaman Big Papi.

5

David was born in the Dominican Republic in 1975. He was signed by the Seattle Mariners in 1992.

David nació en 1975 en la República Dominicana. En 1992, fue contratado por los Marineros de Seattle.

David played for the Minnesota Twins from 1997 to 2002. He was hurt in 2001 and did not play many games.

David jugó para los Mellizos de Minnesota de 1997 al 2002. David no jugó muchos partidos en el 2001 porque estaba lastimado.

9

David joined the Boston Red Sox in 2003. He is a DH or designated hitter for the Red Sox.

David llegó a los Medias Rojas de Boston en 2003. David es el bateador designado de los Medias Rojas.

David is a left-handed hitter.
It is hard to strike him out.

David batea del lado izquierdo.
¡Es muy difícil ponchar a David!

David is known as a clutch hitter. A clutch hitter can hit the ball when it is most needed.

A David se le conoce como un bateador oportuno. Un bateador oportuno puede batear la pelota en los momentos más importantes.

15

The Boston Red Sox won the 2004 World Series. David hit the ball many times.

Los Medias Rojas de Boston ganaron la Serie Mundial en 2004. David bateó la pelota muchas veces.

David hit forty-seven home runs in 2005. He had never hit so many home runs in 1 year!

David bateó 47 jonrones en 2005. ¡David nunca había bateado tantos jonrones en un año!

19

David was named team MVP
for the second year in a row in
2005. That means he was the
most valuable player!

David fue elegido el Jugador
más Valioso de su equipo en
2005. David recibió este honor
dos años seguidos.

21

Glossary / Glosario

designated hitter (DEH-zihg-nay-tuhd HIH-tuhr) A player who bats in place of the pitcher.

home run (HOHM RUN) A hit in baseball that allows the batter to run around all four bases and score a run.

strike (STRYK) To swing at the ball and not hit it. To not swing at the ball when you should try to hit it.

World Series (WUHRLD SEER-eez) A number of games played every year to decide the best baseball team.

---

bateador designado (el) Jugador que batea en lugar del *pitcher*.

jonrón (el) Batazo que sale del campo y permite que el bateador recorra todas las bases para anotar una carrera.

ponchar Descalificar al bateador tras hacerlo abanicar tres veces al tratar de batear la pelota.

Serie Mundial (la) Partidos que se juegan cada año para determinar el mejor equipo.

Resources / Recursos

BOOKS IN ENGLISH / LIBROS EN INGLÉS

Gibbons, Gail. *My Baseball Book*. New York: Harper Collins Publishers, 2000.

Savage, Jeff. *David Ortiz*. Minneapolis, MN: Lerner Publishing Group, 2006.

BOOKS IN SPANISH / LIBROS EN ESPAÑOL

Suen, Anastasia. *La historia del béisbol*. New York: Rosen Publishing/Editorial Buenas Letras, 2004.

Index

Índice